Penpals for Handwriting

Workbook

5

Name _____ Class _____

Unit 1

Introducing sloped writing in letter families

1 Trace and write the letters.

l i t u j y   r n m h b k p

c a d o s g q e f   v w x z

2 Write the letters in alphabetical order.

3 And again. Faster.

Check:
- the slope of your handwriting
- your letters are in correct alphabetical order.

Find two letters to tick and two to improve.
Rewrite them.

Practising sloped writing: diagonal join to ascender

S Unit 2

1 Trace and write the joins.

th ch al el at   th ch al el at

2 Trace and write the words.

their   they're   there

3 Choose a word from above to fill each gap. Rewrite the sentence.

"We put them over _____ but _____ not _____ now."

Check:
- the slope of your handwriting
- your use and spelling of the homophones.

Find two sloped joins to tick and two to improve.
Rewrite them.

3

Unit 3 S — Practising sloped writing: diagonal join, no ascender

1 Trace and write the joins.

a   ai   ay   eigh   *a   ai   ay   eigh*

2 Trace and write the words.

Rain, rain go away.

3 Choose a spelling to complete each word.

There are too many compl__nts about the st__te of the subw__s: ____teen this week!

4 Write the text.

Check:
- the slope of your handwriting
- your use and spelling of words with the *ai* sound.

Find two sloped joins to tick and two to improve. Rewrite them.

Practising sloped writing: diagonal join to an anticlockwise letter Unit 4

1 Trace and write the joins.

ta da as ad ed ea   ta da as ad ed ea

2 Trace and write the words.

accept past heard seen except passed herd scene

3 Write the word that matches each definition.

_____ = to receive something like a present.

_____ = a new action in a play.

_____ = group of elephants.

4 Now write a definition for one of the other words.

Check:
- the slope of your handwriting
- your use and spelling of the homophones.

Find two sloped joins to tick and two to improve.
Rewrite them.

5

Unit 5 G Practising sloped writing: horizontal join to ascender

1 Trace and write the joins.

wh ol ob of ot   wh ol ob of ot

2 Trace and write the words.

who   which   where   when   whose

3 Choose a word from above to fill each gap. Rewrite each sentence.

The woman, _____ car was stolen, rang the police.
The pterygotus, _____ was a water scorpion, is extinct.

Check:
- the slope of your handwriting
- your use of *wh* words in relative clauses.

Find two sloped joins to tick and two to improve.
Rewrite them.

Practising sloped writing: horizontal join, no ascender   Ⓢ Unit 6

1 Trace and write the joins.

ough _____   *ough* _____   *ough* _____   *ough* _____

2 Trace and write the words.

thought   *through*   *thorough*   *although*

3 Choose a word from above to fill each gap.

_____ it was raining, we wanted to go for a walk _____ the woods. We _____ about the route. We were _____ly soaked.

4 Write the text.

_____

_____

Check:
- the slope of your handwriting
- your spelling of *ough* words.

Find two *ough* words to tick and two to improve. Rewrite them.

_____

_____

7

Unit 7 S **Practising sloped writing: horizontal join to an anticlockwise letter**

1 Trace and write the joins.

od *od*

os *os*

og *og*

od *od*

2 Trace and write the words.

explode

curiosity

apologise

production

3 Fill in the gaps.

Noun	Verb
explosion	*explode*
occurrence	_____
_____	_____
_____	*apologise*
_____	_____
_____	*accommodate*

4 Write a sentence using two of the words from above.

_____

_____

_____

_____

Check:
- the slope of your handwriting
- your spelling of words ending -*ence* and -*ise*.

Find two sloped joins to tick and two to improve. Rewrite them.

Practising sloped writing: joining from r S **Unit 8**

1 Trace and write the joins.

re

rh

ra

ro

ru

2 Trace and write the words.

relevant

rhythm

radius

rodent

rumour

3 Rewrite the words in alphabetical order.

rotate

relevant

rhythm

ritual

recognise

rustle

radius

rhyme

recommend

Check:
- the slope of your handwriting
- your alphabetical order.

Find two sloped r joins to tick and two to improve. Rewrite them.

9

Unit 9 G P — Practising sloped writing: joining from s

1 Trace and write the joins.

sc   so   sa   sh   st

2 Trace and write the words.

screamed   something   said   shoes   stayed

3 Choose any words to fill each gap. Rewrite each sentence. Add punctuation to show the subordinate clauses. Write how many of each type of punctuation mark you used.

The _____ who screamed was _____

The _____ whose shoes were _____ was _____

I used: [ ], [ ].

Check:
- the slope of your handwriting
- your use of punctuation to mark the subordinate clauses.

Find two sloped s joins to tick and two to improve. Rewrite them.

End-of-term check — Unit 10

1 Trace and write the words. Award yourself one point for each accurately written word.

therefore   *scream*   *allowed*   *whose*   *although*

explosion   *accommodation*   *rhyme*   *something*   *scorpion*

/10

2 Finish and write the words. Award yourself one point for each accurately completed word.

compl__nts   *wh__e*   *they'__*   *whi__*

alth__   *expl__*   *ap__ise*   *rec__d*

/8

3 Find two words to tick for neatness of the slope and two to improve. Rewrite them.

/2   Mark and score.   /20

Unit 11 Practising sloped writing: proportion – joining from *f* to ascender

1 Trace and write the joins.

fl   ft   fla   fly   fle   flo

2 Trace and write the words.

flag   flavour   sifting   reflect   float

3 Rewrite the text using commas, full stops and capital letters to clarify the meaning.

the safety flag was flying at the beach people were drifting on surfboards inflatables and floats the sky was reflected in the clear water

Check:
- the slope of your handwriting
- the height of ascenders and length of ascenders
- the punctuation.

Find two sloped *f* joins to tick and two to improve.
Rewrite them.

Count the number of punctuation marks you used: | , | | . | |

Practising sloped writing: size – joining from *f*, no ascender S **Unit 12**

1 Trace and write the joins.

fa

fo

fi

2 Trace and write the words.

father

farther

forth

fourth

profit

prophet

3 Choose from the homophones to fill each gap. Rewrite the sentences.

The _____ I travel the more I want my _____.

After the _____ visit, I was tired of going back and _____.

A _____ foretells the future but a _____ is an amount of money.

Check:
- the slope of your handwriting
- the ascenders and the descenders
- your spelling of the near homophones.

Find two sloped *f* joins to tick and two to improve. Rewrite them.

13

Unit 13 P

Different styles for different purposes: writing a paragraph

1 Read about the Arctic fox.

Arctic fox
- *small mammal*
- *habitat: Arctic Circle*
- *adult height at shoulder: up to 30cm*
- *summer fur colour: dark grey*
- *winter fur colour: white*
- *diet: omnivore includes lemmings berries eggs insects squirrels*

2 Rewrite these notes using punctuation and layout to make them clearer.

3 Write a sentence about the Arctic fox in your best handwriting.

Check:
- the handwriting used for notes and for best What is different? What is the same?
- your punctuation in your best handwriting.

Find two words to tick and two to improve. Rewrite them.

Practising sloped writing: speed: *ff*   **Unit 14**

1 Trace and write the joins.

ff _____ *aff* _____ *eff* _____ *iff* _____ *off* _____ *uff* _____

2 Trace and write the words.

efficient   *difference*   *affection*   *suffer*

3 Choose a modal verb and a verb phrase and write three sentences.

might	be efficient
should	show affection
will	make a difference
must	suffer in silence

You might have to suffer in silence.

1. _____
2. _____
3. _____

Check:
- the slope of your handwriting
- the spacing between words
- the size of the letters
- the length of descenders and the height of ascenders.

Find two sloped *f*s to tick and two to improve. Rewrite them.

15

Unit 15 S Practising sloped writing: speed and legibility: *rr*

1 Trace and write the joins.

rr   rr   rr   rr

2 Trace and write the words.

referring   preferring   transferring   occurring

3 Complete the table using verb suffixes and inflections.

Noun	Verb	*-ing* form	*-ed* form
occurrence			
preference			
transfer			

4 Write a sentence using one of the verbs.

Check:
- the slope of your handwriting
- your *rr* joins
- your spelling of words with *rr*.

Find two sloped *rr* joins to tick and two to improve. Rewrite them.

Practising sloped writing: size, proportion and spacing: ss

S Unit 16

1 Trace and write the joins.

ss

ess

uss

iss

oss

2 Trace and write the words.

confession

necessary

discussion

permission

possession

3 Write the words in the table.

confession   pressure   classify
necessary   reassure   tissue
business   distress   possession
impossible   discussion possible
admission   permission

ss **sounds like** assess	ss **sounds like** assure

Check:
- the slope of your handwriting
- your ss joins
- your spelling of words with ss.

Find two sloped ss joins to tick and two to improve. Rewrite them.

Unit 17 S

Practising sloped writing: building speed: *qu*

1 Trace and write the joins.

que
que
equ
aqu
qua
qua

2 Trace and write the words.

queue
consequently
frequently
aquatic
equally
quarrel

3 Choose from the *qu* words to fill each gap. Rewrite the sentences.

I _____ visit the _____ centre in town, but the _____ is so long that people start to _____. I am _____ looking online for an _____ good stockist.

Check:
- the slope of your handwriting
- your *qu* joins
- your spelling of words with *qu*.

Find two sloped *qu* joins to tick and two to improve. Rewrite them.

Different styles for different purposes: decorative alphabets S **Unit 18**

1 Use decorative fonts to write the pairs of words in a way which shows their meaning.

herd	*heard*	*father*	*farther*

guessed	*guest*		

Choose your own pair of confusable words. Write them here. Add pictures below.

_____ _____

Check:
- your spelling of each word within the picture
- your presentation.

Tick the one you are most pleased with.

Unit 19 G — **Different styles for different purposes**

1 Trace and write the words.

afterwards

underneath

secondly

meanwhile

2 Sort the adverbials into the chart.

once *always* *meanwhile*
afterwards *several* *underneath*
secondly *in the jungle* *nearby*

Adverbials of time (Write in your best handwriting.)	**Adverbials of place** (Write in your usual handwriting.)	**Adverbials of number** (Write in your fastest handwriting.)

3 Write a sentence using some of the adverbials.

Check:
- your different styles of handwriting
  What is the same? What is different?
- adverbials are correctly sorted.

Find two words to tick and two to improve.
Rewrite them.

End-of-term check Unit 20

1 Copy these words.

flavour   forth   fourth   efficient   preferring

necessary   discussion   frequently   queue   nearby

/10

2 Finish and write the words. You have met them all in units 11–19.

a_ection   di_erence   transfe_ing   occur___

impo_ible   rea_ure   a_arium   ___rrel

/8

3 Write your name in your best handwriting.

/2

4 Write notes about two things you need to do this week.

5 Write your initials in decorated alphabet letters.

/3

6 Find two words to tick for a neat slope and two to improve. Rewrite them.

/2

Total: /25

21

Unit 21

Sloped writing: proportion, joining p and b to ascenders

1 Trace and write the joins.

pl

ple

pla

pli

bl

ble

2 Trace and write the words.

plate

couple

complain

dumplings

probably

available

3 Choose from the pl and bl words to fill each gap. Rewrite the sentences.

Winter Warmers

It's _____ true to say that of the _____ crops in winter the most popular are potatoes (my favourite) and sprouts (yuk). I never _____ if there are also a _____ of _____ on my _____.

Check:
- the slope of your handwriting
- your joins from p and b
- your punctuation.

Find two sloped p, b joins to tick and two to improve. Rewrite them.

Handwriting for different purposes: joining from *p* and *b*, no ascender

(G) Unit 22

1 Trace and write the joins.

pr_____   po_____   pe_____   ba_____

2 Trace and write the words.

probably_____   possibly_____   perhaps_____   on balance_____

3 Write a note to a friend. Use adverbs to show that it is unlikely you will be able to meet up.

_____

_____

_____

_____

Check:
- the slope of your handwriting
- your joins from *p* and *b*
- your different styles of handwriting for different purposes e.g. best, notes.

Find two sloped joins from *p*, *b* to tick and two to improve. Rewrite them.

23

Unit 23 S   **Practising sloped writing: parallel downstrokes**

1 Trace and write the joins.

bb _____ bble _____ pp _____ pple _____

2 Trace and write the words.

equipped   apply   appendix   supplement

3 Unscramble the syllables and write the words.

| mint pep per | par ly ent ap | ap ate pro pri | bling squab |

| val ap pro | ca ap tion pli | ate pre ap ci | born ly stub |

Check:
- the slope of your handwriting
- your downstrokes of *pp*, *bb*
- your spelling of the unscrambled words.

Find two words to tick and two to improve.
Rewrite them.

Practising sloped writing: all double letters — Unit 24

1 Trace and write the joins.

bb cc dd ee ff gg ll mm nn oo pp rr ss tt zz

2 Trace and write the words.

disappoint   misspell   reattach   refilled

3 Add a prefix *dis-, de-, re-, mis-* **or** *over-* **to these verbs. Write the verbs.**

_____appear   _____understood   _____lapping

_____arrange   _____connected   _____settled

_____agreeing   _____satisfied   _____filled

Check:
- the slope of your handwriting
- your double letter joins
- your spelling of words with prefixes.

Find two joined double letters to tick and two to improve. Rewrite them.

Unit 25 Practising sloped writing for speed

1 Trace and write the joins.

tial

cial

cial

tial

tial

2 Trace and write the words.

partial

special

social

essential

torrential

3 Unscramble the syllables and write the word.

fi of cial _____

cial fi ti ar _____

den con tial fi _____

ten po tial _____

re tial si den _____

4 Write the spelling rule for adding cial **or** tial.

_____

_____

_____

Check:
- the slope of your handwriting when written at speed
- your spelling of words with tial, cial.

Find two words to tick and two to improve. Rewrite them.

Practising sloped writing for fluency — Unit 26

1 Trace and write the joins.

ie   ie   ie _____   *ei   ei   ei* _____

2 Trace and write the words.

achieve   belief   mischief   neither   receive   ceiling

_____   _____   _____   _____   _____   _____

3 The spelling rule is 'i before e except after c when the vowel sounds like ee'. Sort the words into the chart. Underline words that break the rule.

ancient   weird   ceiling
perceive   protein   vein
conscience   leisure   sieve
deceive   receive   field

ie	cei	ei

Check:
- the slope of your handwriting
- the flow of your handwriting
- your spelling of *ie* and *ei* words.

Find two words to tick and two to improve. Rewrite them.

Unit 27 ⓢ   **Personal style**

1 Trace and write the joins.

st ____   bt ____   mn ____   kn ____   wr ____   is ____   th ____

2 Write the sentence.

I doubt that the plumber is also a wrestler.

3 Write these words in your own style. Underline the silent letter(s) in each.

autumn   gnawing   castle   business

asthma   wrinkled   subtle   island

knight   where   friend   knowledge

Check:
- you found the silent letters
- the neatness of your writing at speed
- your personal style. How can you describe it?

Find two words to tick and two to improve.
Rewrite them.

Handwriting for different purposes: print alphabet — Unit 28

1 Write the print alphabet.

a b c d e f g h i j k l m

n o p q r s t u v w x y z

2 Use the phrases to label the diagram. Print.

tail for propulsion
dorsal fin for steering
gill for breathing
eye for seeing
mouth for eating

Check:
- your print letters:
    - have no exit flicks
    - are upright
    - are in proportion and well spaced
- you have not used capitals or full stops for the labels.

Find two words to tick and two to improve.
Rewrite them.

Unit 29 — Assessment

Question: How can you tell which end of a worm is the head?
Answer: Tickle the middle and see which end smiles.

1 Write the joke in fast, fluent sloped writing.

_____
_____   /4

2 Write the joke in print lettering.

_____
_____   /4

3 Write the joke in capitals.

_____
_____   /4

4 Write the joke in quick notes.

_____
_____   /4

5 Write the joke in your preferred personal style.

_____
_____   /4

6 What I need to improve:

_____

Total: /20

Capitals

Unit 30

1 Write the alphabet in capital letters.

a b c d e f g h i j k l m

n o p q r s t u v w x y z

2 Write the names in alphabetic order. Use capital letters and lower case letters.

sandra
risala
anya
andrew
tee-jai

reda
sanjay
troy
andrea

Register

Find two words with joins to tick and two to improve. Rewrite them.

Certificate

for completing

PENPALS for
Handwriting 5

awarded to

NAME
_____

DATE _____ SIGNED _____

University Printing House, Cambridge CB2 8BS,
United Kingdom

One Liberty Plaza, 20th Floor, New York,
NY 10006, USA

477 Williamstown Road, Port Melbourne,
VIC 3207, Australia

4843/24, 2nd Floor, Ansari Road, Daryaganj,
Delhi – 110002, India

79 Anson Road, #06–04/06,
Singapore 079906

Cambridge University Press is part of the
University of Cambridge.

It furthers the University's mission by
disseminating knowledge in the pursuit of
education, learning and research at the
highest international levels of excellence.

Information on this title: www.cambridge.org

© Cambridge University Press 2015

This publication is in copyright. Subject to statutory
exception and to the provisions of relevant collective
licensing agreements, no reproduction of any part may
take place without the written permission of Cambridge
University Press.

First published 2015
20 19 18 17 16 15

Printed in Poland by Opolgraf

*A catalogue record for this publication
is available from the British Library*

ISBN 978-1-84565-861-8

Acknowledgements

© Cambridge University Press 2015
www.cambridge.org

Illustrations by Matthew Britton
Cover design and layout by me&him
Authors: Gill Budgell and Kate Ruttle